Made Simple

ELECTRICITY

Mike Lawrence

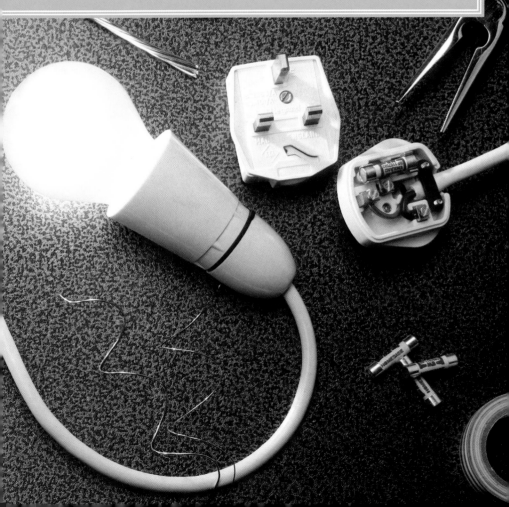

Made Simple

ELECTRICITY

Mike Lawrence

Bloomsbury Books
London

Made Simple

ELECTRICITY

Page 2:   Household electrical appliances.

This edition published in 1994 by Bloomsbury Books,

an imprint of The Godfrey Cave Group,
42 Bloomsbury Street, London. WC1B 3QJ

Under license from Harlaxton Publishing Limited
2 Avenue Road, Grantham, Lincolnshire, NG31 6TA, United Kingdom.
A member of the Weldon International Group of Companies.

Publisher: Robin Burgess
Design and Coordination: Rachel Rush
Editing: Martyn Hocking
Illustrator: Clive Spong, Linden Artists
Photography: Chris Allen, Forum Advertising Limited
Typesetting: Seller's, Grantham
Colour Reproduction: GA Graphics, Stamford
Printing: Imago, Singapore

British Library Cataloguing-in-Publication data.
A catalogue record for this book is available from the British Library.
Title: Made Simple - ELECTRICITY
ISBN: 1-85471-347-7

CONTENTS

The electricity supply is one part of the modern home that seems to strike terror into the hearts of do-it-yourselfers everywhere.

Do-it-yourselfers will clamber about on roofs, knock down walls, plaster ceilings and install their own central heating. Yet they will shy away from any work on their house electricity supply, on the grounds that electricity can kill and so is best left to the experts.

Electricity is dangerous if it is not used safely or treated with due respect, but there are plenty of other do-it-yourself activities that can more easily lead to disaster if they are carried out without due care and attention.

There is nothing to be afraid of as far as electricity is concerned. All you need to work with it safely is a clear understanding of the basic principles, coupled with the patience and skill to work methodically and safely. You need no special skills and few specialist tools, and all the materials you will require are widely available from retail outlets and diy superstores.

Whatever wiring work you are tackling, always remember these basic safety rules:

1: MAKE SURE YOU KNOW WHAT YOU ARE DOING – and can complete the job properly.

2: ENSURE THAT THE POWER SUPPLY IS SWITCHED OFF – at the main switch before starting work.

3: DOUBLE-CHECK ALL CONNECTIONS – to ensure that wires go to the correct terminals and are securely anchored.

4: ALWAYS UNPLUG ELECTRICAL APPLIANCES – before trying to inspect or repair them.

5: NEVER TOUCH ANY ELECTRICAL FITTING OR APPLIANCE WITH WET HANDS – never use electrical equipment out of doors in wet conditions.

6: NEVER OMIT EARTH CONNECTIONS – the only appliances that do not need an earth are non-metallic light fittings and double-insulated appliances and power tools.

OPPOSITE: Atmospheric lighting in a modern open plan dining room.

Electricity must be treated with respect at all times – to do this you must first appreciate the rules and basic principles.

RULES AND REGULATIONS

In the United Kingdom, anyone can do their own wiring work. Professional electricians follow a code of practice called The Regulations for the Electrical Equipment of Buildings.
These regulations are published by the Institution of Electrical Engineers (IEE) and are known as the *IEE Wiring Regulations*, but they do not have the force of law except in Scotland, where they form part of the Scottish Building Regulations.
However, it is essential that do-it-yourself electricians also follow the provisions of the Regulations, to ensure that the system is safe to use. All the instructions given in *Electricity Made Simple* comply with the current (16th) edition of the Regulations.

EARTHING AND CROSS-BONDING

It is essential that every new wiring accessory or light fitting you install is connected to the house's earthing system.
This means connecting the earth conductor in the new cable both to the new accessory or fitting and to the existing circuit wiring at the chosen connection point. If you are installing an electric shower unit in a bathroom (see page 39), you must also ensure that its supply pipework – and any other exposed metalwork in the room – is cross-bonded to the earthing system. To do this you fit a special earth clamp on the pipework and run a 6mm^2 single-core insulated earth cable from it to the earth terminal on the shower unit.

HOW ELECTRICITY WORKS

Electricity can do work – lighting a lamp or driving a motor, for example – only if it can flow round a complete circuit, rather like the water in your plumbing system.
Like water, it will flow through the cable carrying it only if there is a pressure difference between the two ends of the system. What drives electricity is the voltage difference between the supply (live or phase) cable and the return (neutral) cable; this is about 240 volts in the United Kingdom, 220 volts in Australia, New Zealand and the EC, and 110 volts in the United States, Japan and South America.
How much electricity flows through a cable – the 'current' – is measured in ampères (usually shortened to amps), and depends on the 'resistance' to free flow of what lies between the live and neutral parts of the circuit. If resistance is low, the current flow will be high. Substances with low resistance are called 'conductors'. Metals such as copper are among the best conductors, which is why they are used for house wiring work.
Materials with high resistance to the passage of electricity are called 'resistors', and if the resistance is so high as to impede the flow of electricity completely, the material is called an 'insulator'. The best insulators are plastics, ceramics and rubber.

OPPOSITE: The electricity supply is a modern essential for today's lifestyle

THE HOUSE SUPPLY

Your electricity supply originates at the local supply transformer and runs to your house through an underground or overhead power supply.

Shortly after entering the house, the supply terminates in a sealed box called the service head or cut-out (1). This contains a large fuse which is there to prevent the house wiring from demanding more current that the supply cable can safely carry without overheating, and which will 'blow' if its current rating is exceeded.

From the cut-out, two large single-core cables run to the electricity meter (2); if the house uses cheap night-rate (off-peak) electricity there will be a dual-rate meter and time clock instead of the conventional meter. Up to and including the meter, all the supply equipment is the property of the electricity supply company, and must not be tampered with in any way.

From the meter, two more single-core cables run to the main on/off switch and distribution centre of the dwelling – what everyone calls the fuse box (3). In a house or flat with an old-fashioned wiring system, the main switch may be in its own box, with cables running from it to individual fuse-boxes, each controlling an individual lighting or power circuit. In a modern home, everything is concentrated into a fuse-box that is called a consumer unit (3).

PROTECTIVE DEVICES

Every wiring installation is designed for maximum safety, to protect both its users and itself from the consequences of an electrical fault.

For example, if the insulation between the live and neutral conductors of the flex to an appliance breaks down, current will be able to pass from one to the other instead of flowing through the appliance. The result is a short circuit; this generates a lot of heat which could start a fire. Another fault that can occur is when something metallic, such as the casing of an appliance, comes into contact with a live conductor, perhaps due to a loose connection. This might give an electric shock to someone touching it as current flows through their body to earth instead of safely on round the system. Protective devices are installed to prevent faults like these having serious consequences.

The first is to provide a continuous electrical conductor all round the house wiring system which is then connected to earth. How earthing works can be difficult to grasp. Electricity normally completes its circuit by flowing back to the local supply transformer and then to earth, rather like used water running down a drain. If it gets out of the system where it should not – a 'leak' due to faulty insulation, for example – it needs an alternative path to earth, and this is the purpose of the earth conductor (4) in all home wiring cables and flexes.

The second protective device cuts off the flow of electricity if the demand for current becomes too great, a fault known as overloading. This happens if too many appliances are plugged into a circuit, and also if a fault, such as a short circuit or current leaking to earth, occurs. The oldest such device is the wire fuse (5), designed to melt and cut off the supply if the current flow becomes too high, but this has now been superseded by electro-mechanical devices called circuit-breakers. These switch themselves off under fault conditions, and cannot be switched on again until the fault has been cleared.

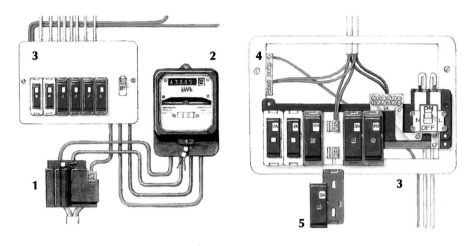

THE FUSE BOX

The fuse-box – or consumer unit on a modern installation – distributes power to the various circuits within the home.

The live supply cable is taken to the system's main on/off switch. This supplies current to a metal bar within the box, and on this bar a protective device – a fuse or miniature circuit-breaker (MCB) – is mounted to protect each circuit. The live core of the circuit cable is connected to the other end of the protective device, while the neutral return core is connected to a separate neutral terminal block within the box. The cable's earth core goes to the earth terminal block, and this is itself connected to earth.

A modern consumer unit, as well as having circuit-breakers instead of fuses to protect each circuit, may also incorporate a separate protective device called a residual current device (RCD). This is often fitted in place of the main on/off switch, and can be switched off in the same way to isolate the whole system from the mains. When switched on, it monitors the balance between the flow of current in the live and neutral sides of the circuit, which should be equal if all is well with the system. If a current leak occurs, for example, because faulty insulation has allowed current to flow to earth through the system's earth conductor, the RCD will switch off the supply automatically. It therefore prevents a fire in the system caused by leaking current and, equally importantly, also protect the users. Anyone touching something live will receive a shock, but the RCD will detect the current flowing through the person's body to earth, and will cut off the supply within milliseconds – fast enough to prevent the shock from being fatal.

![Made Simple]

Made Simple

Made Simple

Made Simple

Made Simple

Made Simple

LIGHTING CIRCUITS

Most homes have two lighting circuits, so that if the protective device on one cuts off the supply, the house is not plunged into total darkness.

The circuit is wired up as a radial circuit, with the circuit cable running from the fuse box or consumer unit to each light position in turn, terminating at the most remote light on the circuit. It usually has a current rating of 5 or 6 amps, and is protected by an appropriately rated fuse or MCB.

The actual wiring connections along the circuit can be made in one of two ways.

1: Loop-in Wiring – the circuit cable runs directly to each light and then on to the next, and a cable to the switch controlling the light is wired in at the light.

2: Junction-box Wiring – the circuit cable runs to a series of junction boxes; from each box separate cables are run to the light and to its switch.

While loop-in wiring is more common on modern house wiring systems, junction-box wiring can be combined with it when this makes more economical use of cable. Junction-box wiring is also useful for adding extensions to the existing wiring.

1

2

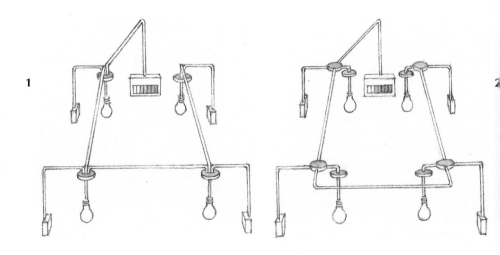

CIRCUITS TO SOCKET OUTLETS

Portable or free-standing appliances with power ratings of up to 3kW are connected to the mains supply via a plug which fits into a socket outlet on the supply circuit.
Modern British wiring installations use a plug with three rectangular pins; this contains a small wire fuse in a cartridge which is designed to protect the appliance in the event of an electrical fault developing within it. The plug can deliver currents of up to 13 amps if fitted with an appropriately-rated fuse, or can be fitted with a fuse of a lower rating to protect low-wattage appliances.
The circuit supplying the socket outlets can be wired up in one of two ways.

3: RING CIRCUIT – the most widely used because it is wired as one. Both ends of the live core of the circuit cable are connected to the circuit's protective device, allowing current to flow either way round the ring to an individual socket outlet, thus increasing the current-carrying capacity of the circuit. Such a circuit has a current rating of 30 or 32 amps, and is protected by an appropriately-rated fuse or MCB. It can supply an unlimited number of socket outlets, but the total floor area of the rooms served by the circuit must not exceed 100m²/1075ft².

4: RADIAL CIRCUIT – supply to sockets with the cable running from one outlet to the next and terminating at the remotest outlet. Such circuits are mainly used where running a ring circuit would involve excessive use of cable – for example, when providing a power supply to a new home extension remote from the fuse-box. The circuit can serve a maximum floor area of 20m²/215ft² if protected by a 20 amp circuit fuse or MCB, and up to 50m²/540ft² if protected by a 30 amp cartridge fuse (NOT a rewirable one) or, a 30 or 32 amp MCB. There is no limit to the number of socket outlets each circuit supplies.

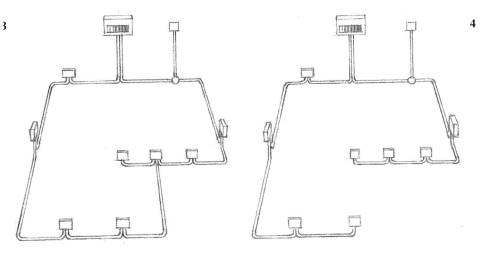

3   4

Apart from supplying socket outlets, ring and radial circuits can also supply so-called fused connection units (FCUs). These allow the appliance flex to be wired directly into the FCU, instead of taking its power supply via a plug and socket, and are used mainly for appliances such as freezers, waste disposal units, cooker hoods and the like which do not need to be plugged in and unplugged regularly.

Older installations used plugs with round pins which were not fused, and had matching socket outlets which came in three sizes to match the current demand of the appliance. The smallest, rated at 2 amps, was for lamps and appliances such as radios. The second, rated at 5 amps, was for larger appliances without heating elements. The third, rated at 15 amps, was for electric fires and the like. Each socket outlet was originally wired individually to its fuse-box, where an appropriately-rated circuit fuse provided the only protection in the event of an electrical fault. However, such systems have often been extended as demand for additional outlets increased, and may no longer be safe.

If you have such a system, get it checked over by a professional electrician before carrying out any work on it yourself.

BELOW: An abundance of small electrical appliances in a modern kitchen.
OPPOSITE: Stylish cooker hoods and hobs in an integrated environment.

Elizabeth Whiting Associates

CIRCUITS TO OTHER APPLIANCES

Large appliances such as cookers, showers and immersion heaters consume more current than a ring or radial circuit can supply, and so have their own individual circuits.

These run from a fuse or MCB in the fuse-box or consumer unit, and have current ratings to match their needs. These range from 15 or 20 amps for an immersion heater up to 45 amps for a powerful cooker or shower. Each circuit cable runs to a double-pole (DP) switch that interrupts both the live and neutral sides of the circuit, allowing the appliance to be completely isolated from the mains for maintenance.

OUTDOOR POWER SUPPLIES

If you want to use an electrical appliance or power tool outdoors, you can plug an extension lead into a socket outlet inside the house.

However, for safety's sake you should always use a plug-in adaptor containing a high-sensitivity RCD, even if your house has an RCD at the fuse-box, to guard against the risk of shock in what is always a dangerous environment for electricity. New homes have to have a socket outlet containing such an RCD and designated for powering outdoor appliances.

If you want to take a permanent power supply to an outbuilding – a detached garage, a garden shed or a greenhouse, for example – then you must provide a separate circuit to it, run from its own fuse or MCB in the fuse-box or consumer unit. The supply cable can be run overhead or underground (see page 41).

Elizabeth Whiting Associates

Made Simple
TOOLS, MATERIALS
AND TECHNIQUES

There is no substitute for safety at all levels,
at all times, when working on installations.

TOOLS FOR WIRING

You need few specialist tools to do electrical wiring, although you will make extensive use of your general toolkit for things like drilling holes in walls and lifting floorboards.

1: CABLE AND FLEX CUTTERS – side-cutters are ideal, used for trimming cable and flex to length.

2: CONTINUITY TESTER – is useful for checking that there is a continuous current path in components that cannot be inspected visually, such as a cartridge fuse or the cores of flex.

3: PLIERS – for gripping and bending conductors, and for twisting cable cores together to connect to a single terminal. A pair of long-nosed pliers is useful for awkward terminals.

4: SCREWDRIVERS – a thin-bladed terminal screwdriver with an insulated blade, medium and large drivers with tips for slotted and cross-head screws.

5: TORCH – similar to a small miner's lamp, leaving both hands free, is a very practical tool.

6: WIRE STRIPPERS – used to remove the insulation without damaging the conductors inside.

CABLE AND FLEX

You use 'cable' for all fixed wiring work, such as power supplies to new wall lights or extra socket outlets. 'Flex' connects electrical appliances and pendant lamp-holders to the mains supply.

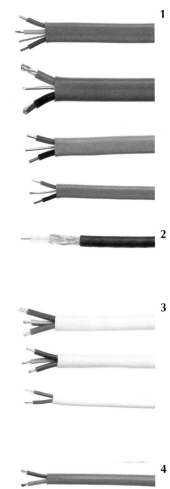

1

1: CABLE – has a tough grey or white PVC external sheath containing the conductors, known as cores. Except in the case of two-way switching arrangements (see page 34), you will be using cable containing two current-carrying cores plus an earth core. The current-carrying cores have colour-coded PVC insulation – red for the live core and black for the neutral. The earth core is bare, but is covered in a slip-on length of green/yellow PVC sleeving whenever it is exposed for connection to a wiring accessory terminal.

The special three-core-and-earth cable used for two-way switching has cores colour-coded red, blue and yellow for identification, plus a bare earth core.

2

2: COAXIAL CABLE – is a special cable that is needed if you want to provide extra TV or telephone outlets – coaxial cable for the former and multi-core telephone cable for the latter (see page 29).

3

3: FLEX – or flexible cord to give it its full name, also has cores contained within an outer protective sheath. This is generally of white PVC, but also comes in black and orange. So-called unkinkable flex, often used on appliances such as irons, has a vulcanized rubber sheath covered in fabric braiding.

Most flex has three cores, each is insulated in PVC and colour-coded so that brown is for live, blue is for neutral and green/yellow is for earth.

4

4: TWO-CORE FLEX – has no earth core, and is used for wiring up non-metallic lamps and light fittings, and also for hand-held appliances and power tools that are double-insulated and so need no earth connection.

Made Simple

CONNECTING CABLE AND FLEX

A|| wiring connections are made at screw-down terminals within wiring accessories, light fittings and plugs.

1 To make a sound connection, the cable or flex sheathing must first be cut back to expose the cores inside; these must then be bared ready for connection to the terminal.

2 When cutting back the outer sheath, remember that the flex or cable cores must not be visible outside the plug or mounting box to which they are connected.

3 Core insulation should run right up to the terminal when the bare conductor has been connected and not be trimmed too short.

4 Bare earth cores within wiring accessories must be covered with a slip-on PVC earth sleeving right up to the terminal.

5 Cable can be connected to flex at light fittings, using strip connectors housed in a mounting-box; this can either be surface-mounted or recessed into the wall or ceiling.

USING CABLE AND FLEX

CABLE – comes in a range of sizes, which represent the cross-sectional area of the conductors measured in square millimetres (mm^2). The commonest are:

$1mm^2$	– for extensions to lighting circuits
$2.5mm^2$	– for extensions to power circuits
$6mm^2$	– for circuits to electric showers

FLEX – comes in several sizes, based on the wattage of the appliance to which the flex is connected. The commonest are:

$0.5mm^2$	– for wiring light fittings
$0.75mm^2$	– for light fittings and small appliances rated up to 1.3kW
$1mm^2$	– for appliances up to 2.3kW
$1.25mm^2$	– for appliances up to 2.9kW
$1.5mm^2$	– for appliances up to 3.6kW

All of the above are sold by the metre length

WIRING ACCESSORIES

This term describes all the various pieces of hardware that are linked together by cable and flex to create your home's wiring system.

1: SOCKET OUTLETS – are the most numerous accessories on a typical installation. These are available in single, double or triple, with or without on/off switches and neon indicators.

2: FUSED CONNECTION UNITS (FCUs) – are used as an alternative to a single socket outlet for appliances which do not get moved around – things like extractor fans. The appliance flex passes into the FCU through a hole in the faceplate, which contains a small fuse carrier holding a cartridge fuse like those fitted in fused plugs. As with socket outlets, the FCU may be switched and may have a neon on/off indicator.

3: DOUBLE-POLE (DP) SWITCHES – are used to control individual appliances, permanently linked to the mains – cookers and electric showers. They are available in wall- and ceiling-mounted versions, the latter cord-operated, in current ratings from 16 to 45 amps.

LIGHT SWITCHES – called plateswitches in the trade, are used to turn lights on/off. The basic type has a single switch on its faceplate, but versions with two, three, four and even six switches are also available (the last two are the same size as a double socket outlet). You can also buy narrow versions called architrave switches, designed to fit on door frames.

4: ONE-WAY SWITCHES – have just two terminals, and operate the light from only that switch.

5: TWO-WAY SWITCHES – have three terminals and are linked to another similar switch to provide two-way switching.

6: CORD SWITCHES – are ceiling-mounted, cord-operated switches for use in bathrooms or wherever cord operation is more convenient than a wall-mounted switch.

7: DIMMER SWITCHES – are light switches that allow you to vary the brightness of the light as well as to turn it on/off, usually by rotating a knob on the switch faceplate.

All these accessories can be fitted on surface-mounted plastic or metal boxes, or flush-mounted over boxes recessed into the wall surface.

8: CEILING ROSES – are used to connect pendant lampholders to the lighting circuit. The flex to the lampholder can either be wired permanently into the rose, which is screwed to the ceiling surface, or can be connected to it via a special plug that fits into a socket in the rose; this is known as a luminaire support coupler (LSC). The big advantage of LSCs is that they allow the light to be taken down easily for cleaning or during redecoration. Similar devices are now also available for use with wall lights.

9: JUNCTION BOXES AND CONDUIT BOXES – are used to make wiring connections on lighting and power circuits, but unlike other wiring accessories are normally hidden above ceilings or beneath floorboards.

Wiring sundries you will need include:

10: PVC SLEEVING (GREEN/YELLOW) – for protecting earth cores within accessories.

11: PVC INSULATING TAPE (RED) – for identifying live cores on switch cables.

12: RUBBER GROMMETS – to fit the holes in flush metal mounting-boxes to stop the cable sheath from chafing.

13: STRIP CONNECTORS – used for making connections to some ceiling and wall lights.

14: MINI-TRUNKING – to carry cable safely either in or over surfaces.

15: CABLE CLIPS – for fastening cable securely to a surface.

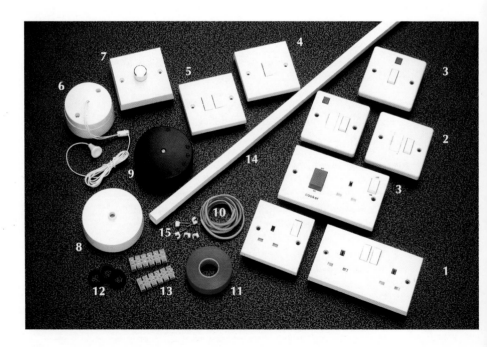

LAMPS AND TUBES

1: GENERAL SERVICE LAMPS – light bulbs, once only pear or mushroom-shaped, now available in a range of squared-off and round shapes including candle and pygmy lamps. They are available with clear or pearl glass in plain and a range of colours, and various wattages.

2: REFLECTOR LAMPS – used mainly in spotlights, have an internal silver coating – either round the base and sides so the light is thrown forwards (an ISL lamp), or inside the crown (a CS lamp) so the light is thrown back into the fitting and then forward by the reflector inside it. Parabolic aluminized reflector (PAR) lamps have armoured glass envelopes and are for outdoor use. All come in a range of colours and wattages.

3: COMPACT FLUORESCENT LAMPS – contain a miniature fluorescent tube and its control gear inside a lamp small enough to fit a standard lampholder. There are several types, some having a cylindrical or spherical glass envelope and others having a cluster of four small glass 'fingers' projecting from the lamp base. They use about a fifth as much electricity as a GLS lamp, and have a lamp life of up to 8,000 hours. They are expensive to buy, but over a period of years cost less than half as much to run as GLS lamps.

4: FLUORESCENT AND FILAMENT LAMPS – in tubular form are available in a range of sizes and wattages. Standard fluorescent tubes are 38mm in diameter, slimline ones 28mm across and miniature tubes 15mm. Tungsten filament striplights are smaller (usually between 220mm and 285mm long) and are mainly used for concealed lighting.

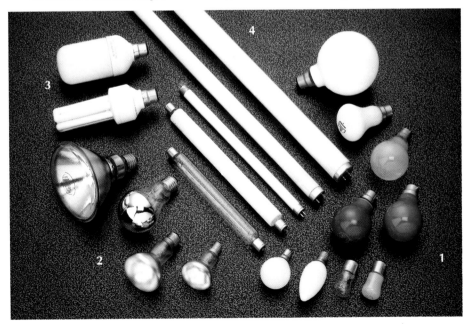

RUNNING CABLE

The only remotely tricky part of extending your home's wiring system is getting new cable from A to B in an unobtrusive way.

1 Ideally cable should be concealed – under floorboards, above ceilings or in channels (called chases) cut in the walls of the room. However, this obviously means wrecking your decorations and probably having to lift fitted carpets or furniture, so it is generally best to temporarily surface-mount the cable and then to conceal it the next time that the room is stripped for redecoration.

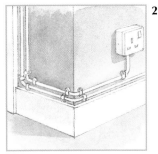

2 You can simply clip white-sheathed cable along the top edges of skirting boards or along the edges of door architraves.

3 A neater solution is to use slim plastic ducting known as mini-trunking. This consists of a U-shaped channel that is stuck or pinned to the wall, and a clip-on cover that conceals the cables once it is snapped into place. Used with surface-mounted accessories, the result is a neat job with the new cables concealed yet readily accessible, and it is far less disruptive than traditional concealed wiring.

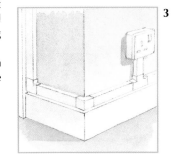

4 When the time comes for the wiring to be concealed, cut chases up and down walls with a sharp brick bolster and a club hammer, clip the cables in place before plastering over them.

5 Lift floorboards so the cable can be threaded through holes drilled in the joists if it must cross them, or can be fed between the joists if it runs parallel to them.

OPPOSITE: Mini-trunking temporarily used to conceal cable.
NEXT PAGE: Stylish ceiling lights in a modern kitchen are discreet but effective.

MOUNTING WIRING ACCESSORIES

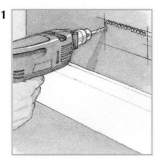

As mentioned earlier, wiring accessories such as light switches and socket outlets can be fitted to flush or surface-mounted boxes. It is obviously simpler to fit a surface-mounted box, screwed to the wall, but a flush box looks much neater. The following fitting instructions are for the mounting only and do not involve live cables.

In masonry walls

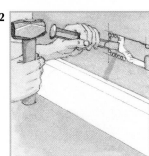

1 The best way of making the recess for the box is to drill a series of closely-spaced holes into the wall to the required depth.

2 Then chop out the resulting honeycomb with a brick bolster and club hammer.

3 Push out one of the pre-stamped knockouts (cable entries) and fit a rubber grommet into the hole to protect the cable from chafing.

4 Screw the box into the recess and make good round it with plaster or filler.

On timber stud partition walls

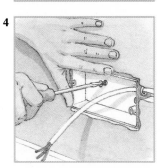

5 It is a simple matter to mark and cut out a square or rectangle of plasterboard using a trimming knife.

6 Use a screwdriver to break out one of the weakened knockouts in the side or base of the box before fitting it.

7 Clip in a special hollow wall box with side lugs that grip the edges of the hole and hold the box in place.

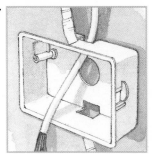

CONNECTING NEW CABLE TO AN ACCESSORY

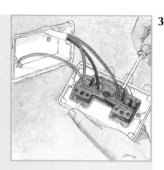

3

1 Turn off the power at the mains.

2 Feed in the cable and strip the sheathing and core insulation to size as required.

3 Then connect the live and neutral cores to the labelled terminals (L and N) on the accessory.
If there is an an earth terminal on the accessory, slip a PVC sleeve over the bare earth core before connection.
If the accessory is metal, link its earth terminal with the terminal in the box – use a short length of earth core from a cable offcut and covered with PVC sleeving.

Light switches are not earthed unless they are metallic

4

4 If the light accessory has an earth, take the earth core to the terminal in the accessory mounting box.

5 Fold the cables neatly back into the mounting box and fit the faceplate to its lugs.

On ceilings

8 Screw ceiling roses and light switches to the undersides of the joists if possible, running the circuit cable down the side of the joist and into the accessory.

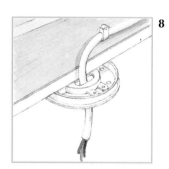

8

9 Otherwise you have to gain access to the void above the ceiling and fix a support batten between the joists; the accessory is then screwed to this through the ceiling surface.

Push the excess cable back into the ceiling void and fit the cover after making the connections.

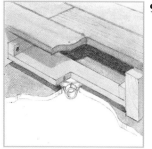

9

Made Simple
TOP 10 WIRING JOBS

There are a number of tasks around the house that enhance our feeling of 'home' – to make life easier or the provision for an appliance more convenient.

The following pages contain a step-by-step guide to some of the jobs most frequently carried out by do-it-yourselfers.

None of these jobs are particularly difficult and all are within the general abilities of the practical householder. However, as with all home improvements, it is commonsense to ensure that personal safety during installation, and user safety after installation, is complete.

Always comply with specific appliance regulations and manufacturers installation instructions. If in doubt, consult a knowledgeable specialist.

ADDING EXTRA TV/TELEPHONE POINTS

Most homes have television sets and FM radios in more than one room, and unless you live in an area of good reception and can rely on set-top or built-in aerials, you will need a rooftop or loft aerial to give good reception.

Adding TV Points

1 The aerial supplies a TV/FM signal via a coaxial cable to the socket outlet. However, to ensure that each outlet does not suffer from loss of signal strength, you need to install a special electrically-powered distribution amplifier, and then to run coaxial cable from this to the various rooms in the house.

2 A single coaxial cable can be used to carry both TV and FM signals if it terminates at a special double TV/FM outlet fitted with a device called a diplexer. These outlets are mounted on a standard single mounting-box.

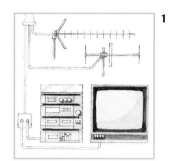

Adding Telephone Points

It is useful to have telephone socket outlets in more than one place in the house.

Householders are now allowed to fit extension socket outlets themselves so long as there is a master plug-in socket outlet installed by a telecoms operator.

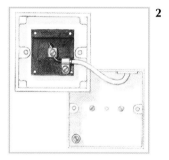

3 Kits are available that contain everything needed for the job – extension outlets, connectors, clips, multi-core cable, detailed instructions and a special tool for connecting the flimsy cable cores to the outlet terminals.

You can install as many extra outlets as you like, but the phones will not ring if you plug in more than four at once. The outlets can be wired using a junction box (A) if this makes more economical use of cable, or in series (B).

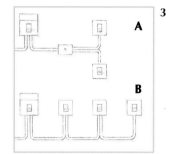

OPPOSITE: Concealed cabling used for safety, yet a convenient and enhanced style of living.

FITTING A DIMMER SWITCH

3

Replacing an existing light switch with a dimmer switch is one of the simplest electrical jobs you can tackle.

There are two points to check before you go to the store buy the new switch.

1: You need to find out whether the existing switch is a one-way or two-way type.
Turn off the power to the lighting circuit.
Loosen the switch faceplate screws so you can ease the old switch away from the wall and see whether it has two terminals (a one-way switch)
or three terminals (a two-way switch).

2: Check the wattage of the light(s) the dimmer will control to ensure it falls between the minimum and maximum operating wattage of the dimmer.

1 **Turn off the power at the mains.**

2 Unscrew the switch faceplate and ease it away from its mounting box. Make a note of which cable core goes to which terminal before disconnecting them.

3 Reconnect the cores to the new switch. The terminals on dimmers are often arranged and labelled differently to those on plateswitches, so follow the maker's instructions carefully.

4 If the dimmer has a metallic faceplate it will also have an earth terminal. You must link this to the earth terminal in the mounting box, so scrounge a few inches of lighting-circuit cable from someone and pull out the bare earth core. Slip a piece of green/yellow PVC sleeving over the two earth terminals and connect them.

5 Fold the cable(s) neatly back into the mounting box, secure the dimmer faceplate to it and restore the power.

INSTALLING A NEW CEILING LIGHT

To replace an existing ceiling rose, check the wiring arrangement at the rose and on the new fitting.

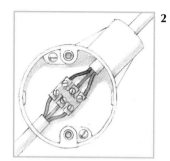

2

If the rose has only one cable and the light has a fixed terminal block (many fluorescent light fittings do), remove the rose, disconnect the cable and connect it directly to the terminal block before securing the light to the ceiling.

If the new light has flex tails emerging from its baseplate or if there is more than one cable at the rose (indicating that loop-in wiring has been used), you will have to remove the rose and replace it with a recessed round conduit box which contains the connections between the light flex and the circuit cables. The light is either screwed to the lugs on the conduit box or the ceiling to hide the box and connections.

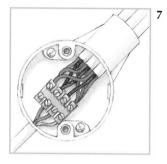

7

1 Turn the power off at the mains.

2 Unscrew the rose cover. Make a note of which cable cores go to which rose terminal, then disconnect them. If only one cable is present and the new light has a terminal block, connect the cores to the block terminals L, N and E.

3 Screw the fitting to the ceiling – screw into the joist to which the original rose was secured.

To fit a recessed conduit box

4 You need access to the ceiling void from above, either through a loft or lift a floorboard in the room above.

5 Remove the rose and draw the cables into the void. Drill a hole between the joists to mark the new light position. Mark around the conduit box position then use a padsaw through the drilled hole to cut round the outline of the box.

6 Fit a piece of wood between the joists, and nail a short batten to each end. Wedge the wood between the joists over the hole and offer up the conduit box to check that its lip will be flush with the ceiling surface. Adjust the level of the support, then nail through the battens into the joist sides to secure the support in place. Screw the box to it.

7 Feed the circuit cables into the box, and connect them to strip connectors as shown. Attach the flex cores from the new light to the strip connectors and push any excess cable back into the ceiling void.

8 Screw the light to the lugs on the conduit box if its baseplate has 51mm fixing holes, or to the wooden support.

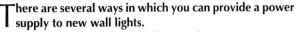
INSTALLING WALL LIGHTS

2

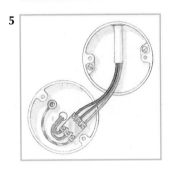

5

There are several ways in which you can provide a power supply to new wall lights.

The method you choose will depend on:

1: How easy it is to gain access to the existing wiring?

2: What sort of switch control do you want?

3: How much are you prepared to disrupt your existing decorations?

The two ways suggested here are the simplest. Unless you are redecorating the room at the same time as fitting the light(s), it is easiest to run the cable to them in surface-mounted mini-trunking, and to bury it in a chase cut in the wall surface when you next redecorate.

Option 1

Take a power supply for the new light from an existing ceiling rose in the same room. The new light will be controlled by the rose's switch.

1 Turn the power off at the mains.

2 Connect the branch cable to the rose as shown, run it across the ceiling to a point immediately above the new light position and pass it down through a hole in the ceiling.

3 At the chosen light position, chop out a recess for a round conduit box and secure it in place. If the wall is a plasterboard wall, fit a slim architrave partition wall box in a hole cut in the plasterboard.

4 Cut a chase in a solid wall, clip the cable into it and feed it into the conduit box. With plasterboard walls, feed the cable down inside the wall and into the architrave box. Alternatively, use surface-mounted mini-trunking.

5 Connect the cable cores to the flex tails on the wall light using strip connectors as shown. Then fold the cable into the box and secure the light, either to the box lugs or to the wall surface, so that its baseplate conceals the box.

OPPOSITE: Wall lights in use in a bathroom to illuminate a mirror and create a warm atmosphere.

Option 2

Take a power supply from a conveniently-sited socket outlet. The new light is controlled by its own switch.

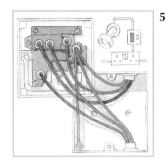

5

1 Turn the power off at the mains.

2 Run a spur cable from a suitable socket outlet (see page 36) to a point immediately above or below the new light position, whichever is more convenient.

3 Fit a mounting box for the light as in Option 1 step 3, and run in the cable as in step 4.

4 Just before the cable reaches the mounting box, fit a mounting box for a switched fused connection unit, which will control the light.

5 Connect the spur cable to its 'FEED' terminals. Then connect a short length of 1mm² lighting cable to the 'LOAD' terminals and run it on to the light's mounting-box.

6 Connect it to the light and secure the light to the wall as in Option 1 step 5.

7 Fit a 5 amp fuse in the fuseholder of the connection unit, and fit this to its mounting box.

Elizabeth Whiting Associates

PROVIDING TWO-WAY SWITCHING

Most lights are controlled from just one switch position, using a one-way switch with two terminals on its faceplate. If you want control from two positions, you have to replace the existing switch with a two-way switch (this has three terminals), and run special three-core-and-earth cable from it to the new switch position, where another two-way switch is fitted to complete the new wiring.

1 Turn off the power at the mains.

2 Unscrew the faceplate of the original switch and disconnect the switch cable.

3 Reconnect the existing switch cable cores to the new two-way switch.

   If the top terminal at one end of the terminal block on its own is marked C, use the two terminals next to each other at the other end of the block marked L1 and L2.

   If the lone terminal is marked L1 use L2 and L3.

4 Run three-core-and-earth cable from the existing switch to the new switch position, running it up the wall and across the ceiling void or down the wall and beneath the floorboards, depending on which route is more convenient.

5 Connect the cores of the three-core-and-earth cable to the two switches as shown.

At each switch, the red core goes to the lone top terminal.
The blue and yellow cores to the bottom two terminals.
Earth cores go to the mounting-box earth terminal.

6 If the switches have metal faceplates, link the faceplate earth terminal to the one in the box with a short length of sleeved earth core.

5

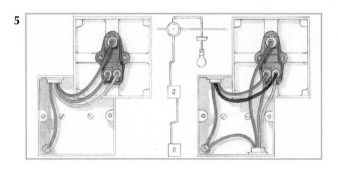

CONVERTING SINGLE SOCKET OUTLETS

If you need more socket outlets and most of the ones you have are single outlets, you can gain extra capacity by converting them to double or triple outlets without having to do any extra wiring work. Select from the options below, for socket that are either flush- or surface-mounted.

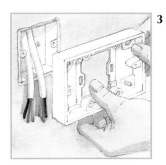

1 Always start by turning off the power.

2 Unscrew the existing socket faceplate and disconnect the cable cores.

Option 1 – new for old surface-mounted outlet

3 Remove the old mounted box. Remove the knockout in the new larger box, so that the cable(s) can be fed in.

4 Screw the new box to the wall and connect the cable cores – red to L, black to N and earth to E.

Option 2 – flush-mounted for surface-mounted outlet

Note that this works only if there is sufficient cable within the original box to reach the new faceplate terminals.

5 Fit a twin converter frame over the existing flush box, screwing the frame to the lugs in the original box.

6 Connect the cable cores to the new outlet – red to L, black to N and earth to E and screw it to the frame.

Option 3 – a new flush-mounted outlet

Care must be taken over the box position to ensure the existing cable cores reach the terminals on the new outlet.

7 Remove the original surface or flush box. Mark the outline of the new mounting box on the wall.

8 On solid walls, chop out the recess. Feed in the cable(s). Screw the new box in place.
   On plasterboard walls, cut out the plasterboard and fit a partition wall box that will grip the sides of the recess.

9 Make the connections to the new socket outlet – red to L, black to N and earth to E.

ADDING EXTRA SOCKET OUTLETS

3
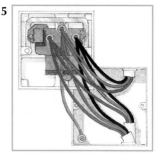

If you want extra sockets where you have none, you can add them by running spur cables – like railway branch lines – from the existing ring circuits.

The only restriction the *Wiring Regulations* impose is that the total floor area of the rooms served by the circuit, including any socket outlets on spurs, must not exceed 100m²/1075ft². You can add extra outlets in one of two ways. In both cases 2.5mm² cable must be used for the spur.

Option 1

5
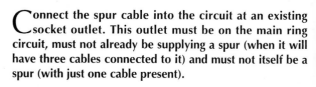

Connect the spur cable into the circuit at an existing socket outlet. This outlet must be on the main ring circuit, must not already be supplying a spur (when it will have three cables connected to it) and must not itself be a spur (with just one cable present).

1 Turn the power off at the mains.

2 Open the chosen socket. If there are two cables present, it is on the ring circuit and can be used to connect in the spur cable.

If it has one or three cables, it must not be used and another outlet will have to be found.

3 At the new socket outlet position, fit a mounting-box and then run cable back by the most convenient route and method to the existing outlet position.

If you do not want to lift floorboards, cable can run round a room to the new outlet, either clipped to the top of the skirting board or concealed in mini-trunking. It can pass through walls to feed a new outlet mounted back-to-back with the existing one.

4 Connect the cable to the terminals of the new socket faceplate and fit this to its mounting box.

5 At the existing socket, connect the new cable cores into the terminals, matching like to like.

All the live (red) cores to the L terminal, black to N, and green/yellow to earth.

6 Fold the cables carefully back into the mounting box and replace the faceplate.

Option 2

Connect the spur cable into the circuit using a three-terminal junction box. Use this method if there is no suitable socket outlet available, or if the cable run from an existing outlet would be inconvenient.

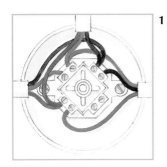

1 Lift a floorboard or two in the room where you want to fit the new outlet, and locate the ring circuit cable. Check that it has enough slack for you to make the connections.

2 **Turn the power off at the mains.**

3 At the new outlet position, fit a mounting box and run cable between the joists to your chosen connection point. If the joists run contrary then drill holes in the centre of the joists and pass the cable through.

4 Connect the spur cable to the new outlet faceplate, then fit this to the mounting box.

5 At the chosen connection point, screw the base of a 30 amp junction box to the side of a nearby joist.

6 Cut the main circuit cable, strip back the sheathing and remove some of the core insulation. Connect the cores, like to like, within the junction box.

7 Prepare the spur cable for connection, and wire it into the junction box, again linking like to like. Sleeve all the earth cores, then fit the box cover.

WIRING 'FIXED' APPLIANCES

2

If you want a power supply for a small fixed appliance – an extractor fan, a cooker hood or a waste disposal unit – you can plug it into a nearby socket outlet.

It is better to give this type of appliance a permanent connection to the socket circuit, using a wiring accessory called a switched fused connection unit (FCU). This allows you to switch the appliance off for maintenance or repair.

The flex is wired directly to terminals, it cannot be accidentally disconnected, and the unit contains a cartridge fuse to protect the appliance. The FCU power supply is from a spur cable, connected to the ring circuit in the same way as the spur for an extra socket outlet (see page 36).

1 Install the appliance, then decide on a position for the FCU. Fit a mounting box for it, then plan the cable route back from it to the ring circuit. Run the cable by the most convenient method and route.

2 At the FCU, connect the spur cable to the 'FEED', and the appliance flex to the 'LOAD' terminals. Secure the flex sheath in the cord grip provided.

3 Fit the FCU to its mounting box. Check that the fuse is the correct rating for the appliance; fit a 3 amp fuse if its wattage is less than 720W, a 13 amp fuse if more.

4 **Turn off the power at the mains.** At the connection point, link the spur cable to the ring circuit at a socket outlet or using a junction box.

RIGHT: A waste disposal unit, one of today's fixed appliances.

Elizabeth Whiting Associates

WIRING AN ELECTRIC SHOWER

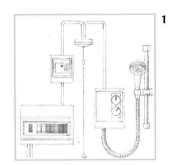

1

One major wiring job to tackle is providing a power supply for an instantaneous electric shower.

This is a straightforward so long as you have available an additional fuseway in your consumer unit. If not, call in a professional electrician to fit and connect an additional enclosure that contains one or two spare fuseways.

1 Install the shower heater unit and plumb it in.

2 Connect 6mm² cable to the shower terminal block and run it up the wall to a ceiling-mounted, cord-operated, 45 amp double-pole on/off switch. The cable may be surface-mounted or, is best, either in a chase cut in the masonry or concealed within a partition wall.

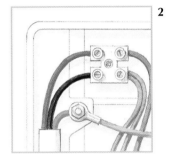

2

3 Fit a special earth clamp to the shower supply pipework, and link its terminal to the earth terminal on the shower unit using 4mm² single-core earth cable, to cross-bond the pipework safely to earth.

4 Screw the mounting box for the ceiling switch to a joist, then pass the cable down the side of the joist through a knockout in the box. Connect it to the 'LOAD' and earth terminals of the switch, then connect a second cable to the 'FEED' terminals; this will run back to the consumer unit by the shortest convenient route (6mm² cable is expensive, so you do not want to waste any).

3

If you have a fuseway available in your consumer unit

5 Turn off the power at the main isolating switch.

6 Move the existing fuseholders along to make a space for a new 45 amp fuseholder or MCB to be fitted next to the main switch – fuseholders must be arranged so that the highest-rated is nearest to the switch (get an electrician to do this if you are unclear how to proceed).

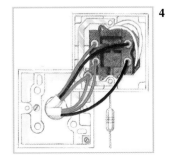

4

7 Connect the cable's live core to the terminal on the fuseholder or MCB, its neutral core to the main neutral terminal block and earth core to main earth terminal block. Restore the power and test the shower.

6 To protect the shower circuit and its users, have an electrician specify and install a residual current device (RCD). This can be installed in the same enclosure as a new fuseway, if he is fitting one, or in its own enclosure.

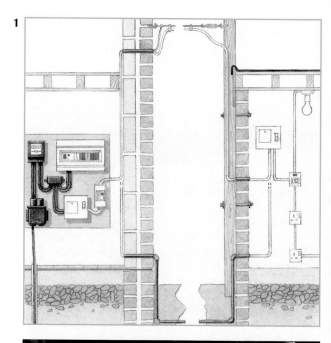

RIGHT: Effective use of electricity outdoors to light the path to an outbuilding.

TAKING POWER TO AN OUTBUILDING

Providing an electricity supply to an outbuilding is similar in principle to wiring an electric shower.

You must fit an independent circuit run in 4mm² cable, either from a 30 amp fuseway in the consumer unit or from one in a separate enclosure if there is no spare fuseway. The circuit must have RCD protection. It runs underground or overhead to the outbuilding, where a small consumer unit is fitted. This distributes power to lights and socket outlets within the outbuilding, and has its own isolating switch so that its circuits can be switched off from within the building.

Plan the cable route.

1 IF UNDERGROUND – it must be enclosed in continuously-welded high-impact PVC conduit, and buried to a depth of at least 450mm.

IF OVERHEAD – it needs no support if the cable span is less than 3.5m, but must be supported by a catenary wire over longer spans. It must clear the ground by at least 3.5m, and by 5.2m if it crosses a drive. The cable can run along walls but must not be attached to fences, which could blow down in strong winds with dangerous consequences.

2 Install the cable run. If underground, excavate the trench and slide lengths of conduit over the cable, solvent-welding each one in turn. Lay the conduit in the trench and back-fill it. At the house and outbuilding, run conduit up the walls to convenient entry points, and feed the cable ends through the walls.

3 WITHIN THE OUTBUILDING – take the cable to the terminals of the new consumer unit. Use a 20 amp fuseway to supply a radial circuit for the socket outlets in the building, and the 5 amp fuseway to supply a lighting circuit.

4 AT THE HOUSE – run the cable to an in-line high-sensitivity RCD and then to the circuit fuseway.

If you have a fuseway available in the consumer unit:

5 Turn off the main isolating switch and connect the cable in as described in 5 to 7 on page 38.

If you do not have a spare fuseway:

5 Get a professional electrician to install an enclosure with two fuseways and fit an RCD – the power supply to it and the existing consumer unit will have to be reorganised.

Made Simple
TROUBLESHOOTING

It is inevitable that from time to time there will be a problem with some appliance or another.

The secret to electrical repairs is to be thorough and methodical in your approach as you systematically eliminate elements of the problem to trace the fault.
The following pages contain some of the more frequent faults. By adopting the basic structure in these examples will assist your understanding of the principle of fault finding.

BELOW: A bedroom vanity unit with all the modern electrical accessories.

TRACING FAULTS – it is essential to trace and correct the cause of an electrical fault.

1: A light does not work

A component such as a lamp bulb may have failed, a connection come loose or a fuse may have blown.

1 **Turn off the light switch** – replace the lamp bulb.

2 **Turn off the power** – check the circuit fuse or the MCB. With fuses – remove and inspect the fuseholder; rewire or replace the fuse. With MCBs – switch MCB back on.

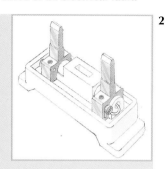

2

3 **Turn off the power** – open ceiling roses and lampholders to check for loose or damaged connections. Remake them if necessary.

4 **Disconnect the power** – check flexes for continuity, and replace damaged flex.

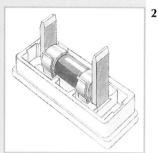

2

2: An appliance does not work

5 Plug another appliance into the same socket outlet. If it works the fault is in the original appliance – go to 6. If it does not work the outlet is at fault – go to 8.

6 Remove and open the plug – check for and remake any loose connections you find. Check the plug fuse with a continuity tester, and replace it if necessary. Replace the top and plug in.

6

7 Unplug the appliance, open its casing/body and locate the terminal block. Check for any loose connections and remake as required.
Check the flex cores for continuity and replace if faulty.

8 **Turn off the power** – open the outlet, check and remake the cable terminals for loose connections.

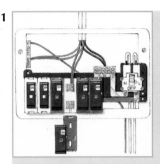

3: A circuit is dead

1 **Turn off or disconnect the power** – check the consumer unit. If the fuse has blown, replace it. Reset the MCB (if it will not reset, the fault is still present).

2 Switch lights on or plug appliances in, one by one. If one blows the fuse, isolate and check it as described above. Check appliance ratings and calculate whether the circuit is overloaded.

3 **Turn off the power** – open accessories and check for loose connections, damaged insulation or signs of overheating. Remake connections, and repair insulation with PVC tape. Replace overheated accessories.

4 If you have drilled through or driven a nail into a cable. **Turn off the power** – replace the fuse or reset the MCB. Expose the damaged cable. In a void you may be able to cut and rejoin the cable using a junction box. Otherwise cut out and replace the damaged cable.

5 If the circuit is still dead, call in an electrician to test the circuit and trace the fault.

4: The whole house has no power

1 Is it a power cut? – check the neighbourhood for signs. YES – notify your area 24-hour emergency number. NO – **Turn off the power** – check and replace the fuses.

2 If you have an RCD – check whether it has tripped off. Reset the RCD – if you cannot, the fault is still present.

3 Are you the only house without power? NO – notify your area 24-hour emergency number. YES – there is either a fault on your main supply cable or your main service fuse has blown. Call the emergency number and ask for an engineer to trace the fault.

EMERGENCY REPAIRS – be prepared for electrical emergencies.

Temporary repairs to things like cracked plug tops, damaged wiring accessories and frayed flex sheathing can be made using PVC insulating tape. A repair is not permanent – replace the damaged component at the earliest possible opportunity.

1: Keep a supply of 3 amp and 13 amp plug fuses, plus a spare plug or two. If your fuses are rewirable – keep a card of fuse wire or spare fuseholders already wired for 5amp, 15amp and 30 amp
2: If your fuses are cartridge fuses – keep a spare fuse of each size close to the fuse-box.
3: It is a good idea to keep a small container holding – all of the above, an electrical screw-driver, an ordinary screwdriver, wire strippers, a small utility knife, a pair of pliers and a torch close to the fuse-box.

REPLACING CIRCUIT FUSES – an emergency kit makes this simple.

If you think a circuit fuse has blown – find your emergency container near the fuse-box. TURN OFF THE POWER – then remove the suspect fuseholder.

1: If it is a rewirable fuse – loosen the terminal screws and remove the remains of old wire.
2: Select wire of the correct rating and cut a new length. Feed it down the protective sleeve, then wind each end around its terminal. Tighten the screws and snip off any excess.
3: If it is a cartridge fuse – test it with a continuity tester and, if it has failed, fit an identical replacement. Replace the fuseholder and restore the power.

In the absence of a proper fuse – NEVER use any other metallic object (nail, paper clip, aluminium foil) to restore power. The circuit will not have any fuse protection, and your dangerous action could actually kill someone.

REPLACING APPLIANCE FLEX – an appliance with a damaged flex is dangerous.

If an appliance flex is damaged or too short for convenient use – replace it. Unplug the appliance from the mains, then open the plug and the appliance casing.

1: Disconnect the old flex – from the plug and the appliance's terminal block and release it from any protective grommets in the appliance. Take the flex with you when you buy the replacement, to ensure that you get the correct size and type. Remember that double-insulated appliances need two-core flex.
2: To fit the new flex – strip the sheathing to expose the cores. Strip away their insulation. Feed the flex through any protective grommets.
Connect the cores – brown to live terminals; blue to neutral; yellow/green to earth on the terminal block of the appliance and plug.
Fit the flex in the cord-grip, then close the plug and the appliance casing.

ℳade Simple

REPLACING DAMAGED ACCESSORIES – damaged accessories are dangerous.

If a light switch, socket outlet or other wiring accessory is cracked, temporarily repair the damage with PVC insulating tape and buy a replacement at the earliest opportunity.
1: **Turn off the power at the mains** – unscrew the damaged faceplate.
2: Ease it away from its mounting box – note which cable cores go to which terminals and disconnect them. Discard the old accessory.
3: Connect the cores to the terminals on the replacement and screw the faceplate to the mounting box. Reuse the old mounting screws if the new ones will not thread.

REPLACING AN IMMERSION HEATER

1A
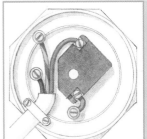

1B
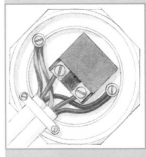

2
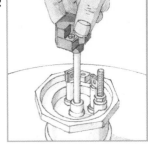

If an immersion heater fails, first check whether the heating element or the thermostat is at fault.

1 **Turn off the power** – to the heater at its isolating switch, remove the heater cover and use a continuity tester on the thermostat terminals, then on the heater terminals.
A – wiring to a single element heater and thermostat.
B – wiring to a dual element heater and thermostat.

2 If the thermostat has failed – disconnect it and slide it out of the heater; fit a matching replacement and reconnect the wiring as on the original thermostat.
If the heating element has failed – turn off the water supply to the hot cylinder and run the hot taps until the flow stops.

3 Attach a length of garden hose to the draincock at the bottom of the cylinder – draw off two or three bucketsful of water – enough to lower the water level inside the cylinder to below the boss.

4 Disconnect the flex – from the heater terminals after making a note of the wiring connections.
Unscrew the old heater – use a hired immersion heater spanner. Heaters tend to get clogged with limescale; if the heater will not budge – use a blowtorch to heat it before trying again with the special spanner. Lift it out and clean round the boss.

5 Slide in the new heater – complete with sealing washer, and screw it in hand-tight. Give it a further half a turn with the spanner.

6 Reconnect the flex and fit the heater cover, then restore the water supply and the power.

Photography props supplied by:

Nina Barough Styling

As credited, photographic material reproduced by kind permission of:

Elizabeth Whiting Associates